# Step
# by
# Step
# to
# Knowing
# God

Written by Narelle Gatenby and
Eric Bird/Illustrated by Peter Oram

AN ALBATROSS BOOK
»»the bible reading fellowship
OPENING THE BIBLE

© Narelle Gatenby and Eric Bird 1988

Published in Australia and New Zealand by
**Albatross Books Pty Ltd**
PO Box 320, Sutherland
NSW 2232, Australia
in the United States of America by
**Albatross Books**
PO Box 131, Claremont
CA 91711, USA
and in the United Kingdom by
**The Bible Reading Fellowship**
Peter's Way, Sandy Lane West
Oxford OX4 5HG, England

First edition published by Monarch Productions 1988
Second edition (completely revised) 1992

National Library of Australia
Cataloguing-in-Publication data

Gatenby, Narelle
Step by Step to Knowing God

ISBN 0 86760 109 4 (Albatross)
ISBN 0 7459 1711 9 (BRF)

1. Bible — Study and teaching
2. God — Knowableness.
I. Bird, Eric. II. Title

231.042

Scripture quotes in this book are from the *Good News Bible*,
© American Bible Society 1966, 1971, 1976.
Printed and bound in Australia by The Book Printer, Victoria

# Contents

# INTRODUCTION:
## *Finding your way*

To help us find our way in the Bible each book is divided into **chapters** and **verses**.

If there is more than one book or letter by the same name, the number 1, 2, or 3 is written before it.

This is the *name of the book*. It tells what the book is about, or who wrote it, or to whom it was written. This is the Good News of Jesus, written by Luke.

The *text* of each book is set out in *columns* for easy reading. Read down the column and continue at the top of the next column.

The *last chapter* on each page is written here.

*Verse* numbers are written in small print.

*Chapter* numbers are written in large print.

*Subheadings* tell you what the next section is about. Not all Bibles have subheadings.

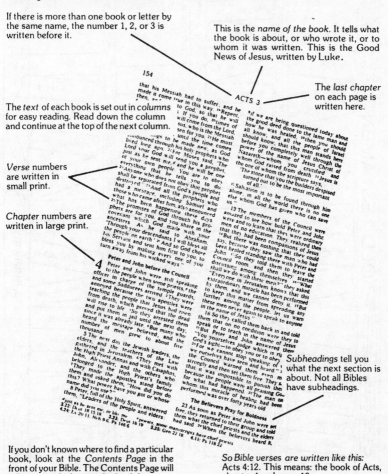

If you don't known where to find a particular book, look at the *Contents Page* in the front of your Bible. The Contents Page will tell you on which *page* the book begins.

*So Bible verses are written like this:*
Acts 4:12. This means: the book of Acts, chapter 4 and verse 12.

# THE BIBLE IS A LIBRARY

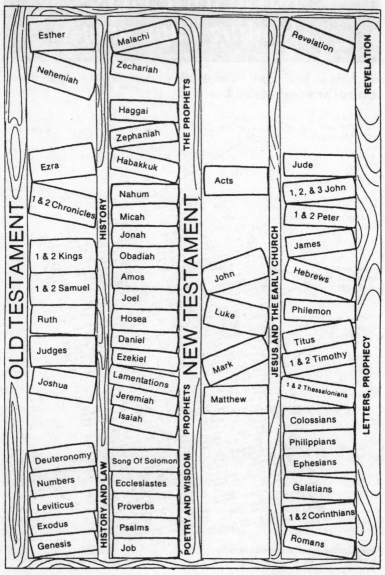

# STUDY ONE:
# *What is God like?*

Is there a God? If there is, what is he like? People have lots of different ideas about God, but how can we know which is true?

When we say we believe in God, what do we mean? Which God do we believe in? Is our God a stern policeman waiting for us to fail again? Is he a Santa Claus figure we expect to come up with all the good things in life when we want them? Perhaps he's a kindly but rather doddery old man who smiles a lot and wouldn't harm anyone!

If there is a God, then surely the first and most important thing we should do is find out what he is like. Is he 'for' or 'against' us? The answer to this matters more than anything else.

It is sad that most people go through life giving these vital questions no more than a passing thought, yet the answer to all of life's other questions depend on how we answer the first one: *What is God like?*

The Bible claims to hold the answers to these questions. It was written over a period of 1,400 years by people who claimed the same incredible thing: there is a God. He has told us what he is like.

## DAY ONE:
## God is Creator
*Genesis 1: 1–10 and 26–28*

1. What does verse 1 tell us about God?

   *created the earth existed from beginni*
   *God has always been. God Active then*
   *Job 33. 4 'The God has made me' + now*

2. What did God think of his creation (verses 4 and 10)?

   *(v.31 very good ) Good*

3. How did God create the universe (verses 3, 6 and 9)?

   *God said By speaking*

4. What is special about mankind (verse 26)?
   (a) We are made like   *God in his image*
   (b) We are made to   *rule over earth, air, sea anim...*
   God made us in his
   image. That doesn't
   mean that we look like
   God or that God looks
   like a person. It means
   we are styled after his
   character. God thinks,
   plans, creates, communi-
   cates, makes choices, has
   emotions, is personal.
   We share in all these
   qualities.

 ## DAY TWO:
## God is great and powerful
*Psalm 104: 1–4*

5. How does the writer describe God (verse 1)?

   *Very great, clothed with splendour*
   *+ majesty*

6.  The forces of nature are very powerful. Has there
    ever been a time when these forces (for example,
    hail, wind, floods or fire) made you nervous?  What
    happened?
    _____House___fires._____
    _____

7.  If nature is powerful, the God who made it is far
    more powerful.  How does the writer of this psalm
    describe God's greatness (verses 2–4)? _Master___
    _of all Creation_____

8.  How should an understanding of God's greatness
    affect the way we live (see verse 1a)?  _We should_
    _Praise the Lord_____

### ✎ DAY THREE:
## God wants us to know him
*Hebrews 1: 1–3 and 2: 1*

9.  This section tells us that God has spoken to us.
    What two ways are mentioned?
    (a)  Hebrews 1, verse 1 _____
    (b)  Hebrews 1, verse 2 _____
    The prophets *told* us about God, but the Son *shows*
    us God.  God has not left it to our imagination to
    guess what he is like.

10. Jesus is God's Son.  What does Jesus show us about
    God (verse 3a)? _____
    _____
    _____

11. If God has spoken, what should we do (chapter 2,
    verse 1)? _____
    _____

## ✎ DAY FOUR:
## God is holy — he hates evil
*Read Psalm 7: 10–17*

12.   What does the writer call God in verse 11?

_____

13.   What does God do for those who obey him
      (verse 10)? _____

_____

14.   What happens to the wicked (verse 11)? _____

_____

15.   If we honour and obey God, how should we
      respond to him (verse 17)? _____

_____

## ✎ DAY FIVE:
## God is love
*Psalm 103: 8–14*

*God is holy — he hates evil. God is love. He gives us time and opportunity to turn away from evil. He knows each one of us personally. He wants you to know him.*

16.   What do the verses below tell us about God's love?
      (a) verse 8 _____
      (b) verse 11 _____

17.   Verses 10 and 11 tell us about God's forgiveness. To
      whom does he give it? _____

_____

18.   If we turn to him for forgiveness, how much are we
      forgiven (verse 12)? _____

_____

19.   What is God like to those who honour him (verse 13)?

_____

## ✎ DAY SIX:
## God is personal

*We have seen that God is not just a force. He is personal. God is personally involved with his world. He knows each one of us personally. He wants you to know him.*

20.   What is the most important thing you have learned about God this week? _____

Why is this important to you? _____

_____

_____

21.   How will this new understanding change your life, your behaviour or your thinking?

_____

_____

Over a period of some 1,400 years, people from different backgrounds (kings, priests, farmers, shepherds, public servants) were moved by God to record his dealings with people. In spite of their different backgrounds and time in history, they all said the same things about God:

*   God is Creator. He is great and powerful.

*   God cares about his creation. He hasn't just made us and then left us alone. God has spoken to us and wants us to know him.

*   God is holy (or perfect) and just. He hates evil. . . but God is love. He has opened the way for us to be his friends.

God has told us what he is like. He is not a 'force'. He is personal: he thinks, plans, makes judgments, loves and speaks.

When we say we believe in God, the question we must ask is: '*Which* God do I believe in?' If it is not the God who is there, as he has shown himself to be in the Bible, then ours is a 'pretend' God — a God of our imagination. That kind of God isn't worth believing in. That kind of God can't touch our lives at all.

The God we must get to know is the God who is there — the true God, the God who loves us and wants us to be brought back into relationship with him. What we believe about God will determine the whole course of our lives, before and after we die. Finding out the truth about God is the most important thing we can ever learn.

# STUDY TWO:
## *What is man like?*

What a puzzle we humans are! At a time when some people are enjoy-ing the highest standard of living ever, two-thirds of the world's population lives in poverty. At a time when human minds have produced intricate medical life-saving equipment, that same intelligence has prepared the means of blowing us apart by nuclear warfare.

We are a riddle. We make marriages and break them. We create fertility drugs and kill unborn babies. We create masterpieces of art and architecture and build slums. We have developed telephone links around the world and yet we fail to communicate within our own families.

When we look into ourselves, we are even more puzzled. With the same mouth we praise and curse. With the same arms we hug and lash out. With the same eyes we watch a sunset and the violence on our television screens.

We are full of contradictions. *Why?*

 ## DAY ONE:
## What went wrong?
*Genesis 2: 15–17, and 3: 1–19*

*The world wasn't always a puzzle. In the beginning, God made it to work in harmony, and people walked and talked with their creator. God was pleased with all he had made (Genesis 1: 31), but something went dreadfully wrong.*

1.  How many rules did God give the man (chapter 2, verses 16–17)? _____

    What was it? _____

2.  How did the snake (Satan) tempt the woman to disobey God (chapter 3, verses 1 and 4)? _____

    _____

    _____

    As soon as the man and woman disobeyed God (verse 6), everything changed for the worse. Relationships were torn apart. Harmony became chaos.

3.  How did the man's and the woman's disobedience affect:
    (a)  what they thought of themselves (verse 7)?

    _____

    (b)  their relationship with God (verse 8)?

    _____

    (c)  their relationship with each other (verses 11–13)?

    _____

    (d)  their relationship with the earth (verse 17–18)?

    _____

4.  What was their future to be (verse 19b)?

    _____

    From that day on, we have all lived in a broken world with broken relationships, separated from God.

DAMAGED!

## DAY TWO:
### It's everyone's problem
*Romans 1: 18–23; 3: 23*

*Most people in our society think they will go to heaven — or at least hope so. Their reason is that they have 'tried their best' and, since God is a decent sort of a bloke, he's sure to understand. They think he'll make allowances for the normal mistakes we all make. But is that how God sees it?*

Read Romans 3: 23

5. Which people are cut off from God by sin? _____

Can any of us go into the presence of God (heaven) because we are good enough? _____
The truth is that not one person will be in heaven with God because he or she deserves to be there. The entry standard is perfection because God is perfect (holy).

Read Romans 1: 18–20.

6. From verse 20, which statement below is true:
   ☐ There is no evidence for the existence of God.
   ☐ Creation makes it clear that there is a God.
   ☐ It is not possible to say if there is a God or not.

7. What can anyone know about God from looking at his creation (verse 20)? _____
_____

 ## DAY THREE:
### It's a 'choice' problem
*Romans 1: 20–23*

*There is no excuse for ignoring, overlooking or rejecting God.*

*The evidence that he exists is there for everyone to see. It's not that we can't know God. We have chosen not to know him.*

8. Is it enough to just believe that God exists (verse 21)? _____

    What else must we do? _____

    _____

9. What are the results of our rejection of God (verses 21b–22)? _____

    _____

*It has been said, 'When people stop believing in God, they will believe anything."*

10. What have people substituted for the true worship of God (verse 23)? _____

11. What are some of the things people in our society choose to worship instead of God? _____

    _____

### ✎ DAY FOUR:
### It's a heart problem
*Mark 7: 20–23*

12. Where did Jesus say that evil comes from (verse 21)?

    _____

13. Can we change people's 'heart condition' (this is, sinful nature) by changing where they live or how much money they have? _____
    Why/Why not? _____

    _____

14. What kinds of actions result from an unclean heart (verses 21–22)? _____

    _____

*There's no use trying to shift the blame. Evil is our own personal problem.*

## ✎ DAY FIVE:
### It's a deadly problem
*Romans 3: 10–20 and Romans 6: 23*

15. In your own words describe the picture of mankind this passage gives (chapter 3, verses 10–18). _____
    _____
    _____

16. Can keeping the Law put us right with God (chapter 3, verse 20)? _____

17. What is the best that the Law can do for us (chapter 3, verse 20)? _____
    _____

18. What is the wage we earn for our sin? (chapter 6, verse 23) _____

*This death is more than physical death. It is 'forever' death: separation from God forever, now and after we die.*

## ✎ DAY SIX:
### God's answer to mankind's problem
*Romans 3: 21–26*

*We have seen that God's standard is perfection, that no-one can possibly reach that standard, and therefore we have no hope of saving ourselves from 'forever' death.*

19. Who has taken action on our behalf to put us right with God (verse 21)? _____

20. How are we able to be put right with God (verse 22)?

21.  What does this new relationship with God cost us (verse 24)? _____

22.  What did it cost Jesus (verse 25)? _____

*Jesus' gift to us of forgiveness and a right relationship with God does not cover everyone whether they know it or not. Like all gifts, it must be received in order to be owned.*

23.  Have you accepted God's gift of forgiveness and eternal life?

It was a tragic day when man and woman first chose to doubt their Creator's love for them and disobeyed him. They thought they had been missing out on something, but finished up with more than they bargained for.

Instead of personal freedom, they gained shame and self-consciousness.

Instead of an open and warm relationship with their Creator, they obtained guilt and fear.

Instead of a world working in harmony with them, they gained a harsh, spoiled environment.

It's been like that ever since and each one of us has made the same choice about God. We are self-centred.

We want things our way, not God's way. We have spoiled God's good gifts.

As a result of our rebellion against God, we have been found guilty of sin. The punishment is death — separation from God now and after we die.

But that's not the end of the story. God loves us dearly and still longs to have us back again. *That's* why Jesus came. God is perfect and just, so he couldn't overlook sin. It must be punished. God is love, so Jesus took the punishment we deserve. Jesus paid so that we could be forgiven *freely*.

Mankind is still the highlight of God's creation. We still bear his image, otherwise society would never function at all, but it is a spoiled, damaged image. It needs renewing and only God can do that.

So. . . who is this Jesus who has done all this for us?

# STUDY THREE:
## *Who is Jesus?*

Two thousand years ago a man was born who changed the course of world history. At about the age of thirty, he began to preach. He gathered around him a mixed bunch of followers from all levels of society, but particularly from among the ordinary working people. Three years later he was dead, executed by the government on a charge of treason. He claimed to be king!

Strange happenings took place after his death. His body disappeared and was never found. His tomb was empty. His followers claimed to have seen him alive.

In spite of opposition and ridicule, these ordinary men and women set about telling the world that God had become a man. They claimed he had died and come back to life. They taught that, because of this man's death, God can freely offer us forgiveness and eternal life.

Who was this man, Jesus, who angered religious leaders, puzzled politicians and won the love of people just like you and me? To answer that question, we must look at who Jesus himself claimed to be.

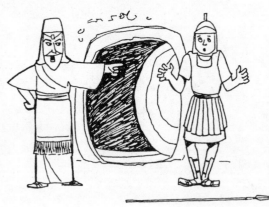

## ✎ DAY ONE:
## Jesus really lived
*Luke 1: 1–4*

1.  Who first told others about Jesus (verse 2)?

    _____

2.  What did Luke think about what they claimed (verse 4)?

    _____

    _____

3.  How did he reach that conclusion (verse 3)?

    _____

    _____

    Luke was a writer of history, not fairytales. Even
    today his writing is respected for its accuracy of
    detail. Jesus really lived — there is no doubt about
    that — but who was he?

## ✎ DAY TWO:
## Jesus was human
*Read the verses below from Luke's Gospel*

These verses are from Luke's Gospel. The word *gospel*
means 'good news'. Each of the verses tells us something
about Jesus which shows he was human. Look up each one
and fill in the spaces below.

4.  (2: 6–7) Jesus was _____

5.  (4: 1–2) Jesus was _____
    by the Devil for forty days.
    In that time he ate nothing. Afterwards he was

    _____

6.  (8: 23) Jesus needed to _____

7. (23: 46) Jesus _____
_____

There was no doubt among those who knew Jesus
that he was as human as they were. There was blood
in his veins just like theirs. He got hungry and tired
like they did. So, is that all he was. . . just a man?

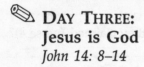 **DAY THREE:**
## Jesus is God
*John 14: 8–14*

*There was no doubt Jesus was human. The disturbing thing was
that he claimed to be God.*

8. What did Philip want Jesus to do (verse 8)?
_____

9. Jesus said many things about himself and God the
Father. What were they?
(verse 9) _____
(verse 10) _____
(verse 12) _____
(verse 13) _____

10. What promise did Jesus make to his friends (verse 14)?
_____

That was a promise he could only keep if he was
God!

Here we see Jesus
claiming to be one
in being with God
the Father and yet
separate from him
— God the Son
(verse 13), fully
human and fully
God.

## DAY FOUR:
## Jesus always existed
*1 John 1: 1–3*

*Jesus didn't begin his existence when he was born in Bethlehem.
He is God. In these verses, John calls Jesus the 'Word of life'.*

11. How long has Jesus, the Word of life, existed (verse 1)?

_____

12. How well did John know this 'Word' (verse 1–2a)?

_____

13. Why did John want everyone to know about Jesus
    (verse 3)? _____

_____

## DAY FIVE:
## Jesus is good news
*Romans 8: 1–8*

14. What is the good news about Jesus (verse 1)?

_____

_____

15. How did God do away with sin's power to
    condemn us (verse 3)? _____

_____

16. Read verses 7 and 8. Which sentence below is true?
    ❏ Mankind is by nature good.
    ❏ Mankind is by nature self-centred (sinful).
    ❏ Mankind is neither good nor bad.
    The good news is so good, because the bad news is so
    bad!

17. How does God see the normal person who lives a

normal life doing what comes naturally (verse 7)?

To those who receive him, Jesus is forgiveness and life. That's the good news.
Those who reject or ignore him are left without rescue — enemies of God. That's the bad news.

18. *A personal question:* Where do you stand? Is Jesus good news or bad news for you?

 ## Day Six:
## Jesus is coming back
1 *Thessalonians 4: 15–18*

19. What will Jesus do in the future (verse 16)?

20. Who will benefit from the Lord's return (verses 16b–17a)?

21. For those who believe in Jesus, there is an encouraging promise. What is it (verse 17b)?

22. What are we to do with this knowledge of the Lord's return (verse 18)?

If someone claimed to be God, we would laugh at the joke, or look for some other behaviour to indicate that this person is mad. We certainly wouldn't react by saying: 'Now look here, I'11 accept that the rest of what you say is true, but I can't accept this one claim of yours that you are God.'
Yet this is the way many people react to Jesus.

They will agree that he was a good teacher, but that is all. Such thinking isn't logical. Because Jesus claimed to be God, we can make one of three conclusions:

1.  *He knew he wasn't God, but he lied.* In that case he was a wicked deceiver.

2.  *He thought he was God, but he was wrong.* In that case he was mad.

3.  *He claimed to be God — and he was.* In that case we had better sit up and take notice!

Which is true? All the evidence points to the fact that something mind-blowing has happened on this planet. The God who made the whole universe — stars, rivers, elephants and snowflakes — cared so much for us that he became a man, lived among us, died for us, overcame death and will come back one day to wrap up earth's history.

Will you be ready to meet him when he does return? We can accept Jesus and find life, or we can reject him and face judgment. With God, there is no middle 'path'.

# STUDY FOUR:
## *What is Jesus like?*

When someone claims to be 'God-become-man', we would expect to see evidence in the daily life of that person. After all, it's easy to make the claim. Proving it is true is another matter!

What evidence would you expect to see in someone who claims to be God? What would you expect him to be like? What would you expect him to be able to do?

A good place to begin is our first study where we thought about what God is like. We saw that he is *Creator*, so we would expect this God-man to have control over creation.

God is *great and powerful*, so we would expect to see evidence of this power.

We are told God is a *communicator*, so he would be wanting to make God known to us.

God is *holy* and hates evil, so any person who claims to be God would need to live a blameless life.

God is *love*, so God-become-man would demonstrate love in everything he did.

Let's look at the life of Jesus as recorded by those who were eye-witnesses and see if he measures up to these expectations.

## ✎ DAY ONE:
### Creator in action
*Mark 4: 35–41*

1. What was Jesus doing during the storm (verse 38)?

   _____

2. Why were the disciples afraid (verse 38)? _____

   _____

3. How did Jesus deal with their fear (verse 39)?

   _____

   After a storm at sea, it takes a long time for the
   water swell to settle down. When Jesus gave his
   command, everything calmed down — including
   the water, immediately!

4. Why were the disciples afraid in the calm (verse 41)?

   _____

5. What evidence does this incident give us that Jesus
   is 'God-become-man'? _____

   _____

## ✎ DAY TWO:
### Power in action
*Mark 5: 21–24 and 35–43*

6. What did Jairus ask Jesus to do for him (verse 23)?

   _____

7. What did Jesus tell Jairus to do when he heard the
   child had died (verse 36)? _____

   _____

8. Which people were allowed to witness this miracle
   (verse 40)? _____

Why do you think these particular people were allowed? _____

_____

9. How did Jesus bring the girl back to life (verse 41)?

_____

_____

_____

_____

10. What evidence does this incident give us that Jesus is 'God-be-come-man'?

_____

_____

✎ DAY THREE:
## Love in action
*Mark 1: 40–42*

11. What had this man understood about Jesus (verse 40)?

_____

12. This man's problem was leprosy. No-one would touch a leper for fear of catching the disease. Jesus was different. How (verse 41)? _____

_____

13. What likeness to God does Jesus show here?
(verse 41) _____
(verse 42) _____

## ✎ DAY FOUR:
## Communication in action
*Mark 4: 1 and 30–34*

14. In this passage, we see Jesus as teacher. Which two groups of people was he teaching?
    (verse 33) _____
    (verse 34) _____

15. What was he teaching them about (verse 30)?
    _____
    _____

A parable is a word picture or a story that teaches us a truth. 'The kingdom of God' is God's rule among mankind.

16. In this parable, what does Jesus say the kingdom of God is like (verses 31–32)? _____
    _____
    _____

## ✎ DAY FIVE:
## Holiness in action
*Mark 11: 15–18*

*We have seen plenty of evidence that Jesus was a kind, under-standing man who took action to deal with pain and need. God is love. That bit we like! But love is not weak and sentimental. God's love is tough love. It won't compromise truth. God is holy. That bit we find hard to take!*

17. What was Jesus angry about (verse 17)? _____
    _____

18. To whom did the Temple belong (verse 17)? _____
    _____

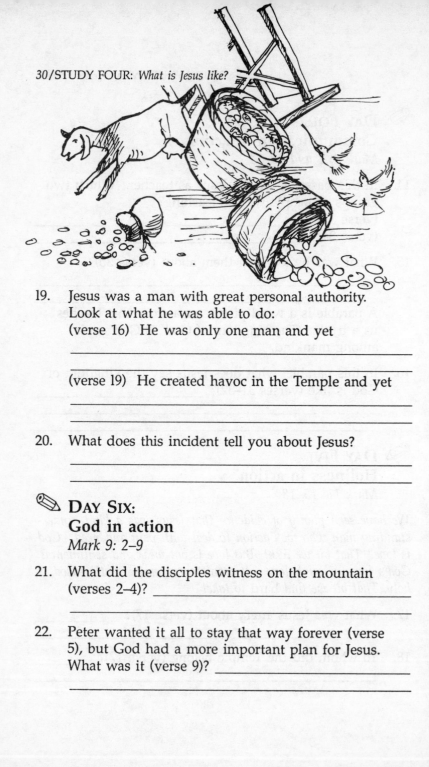

19. Jesus was a man with great personal authority. Look at what he was able to do:
    (verse 16) He was only one man and yet

    _____

    (verse 19) He created havoc in the Temple and yet

    _____
    _____

20. What does this incident tell you about Jesus?

    _____
    _____

## DAY SIX:
## God in action
*Mark 9: 2–9*

21. What did the disciples witness on the mountain (verses 2–4)? _____

    _____

22. Peter wanted it all to stay that way forever (verse 5), but God had a more important plan for Jesus. What was it (verse 9)? _____

    _____

23. Jesus claimed God was his Father. What did God claim about Jesus (verse 7)? _____

_____

24. What evidence does this incident give that Jesus is 'God-become-man'? _____

_____

_____

What do people do when God walks among them? They are drawn to his love and power. They are amazed at his miracles. They're afraid, they get angry, they mock and ultimately they kill him.

Jesus claimed to be God-become-man. He showed by his life and action that he was who he claimed to be. His nature was the nature of God. He demonstrated the power, the love, the communication, the knowledge and the holiness of God.

We can mock, but we do so against all the evidence. 'Give us a sign. . . Perform a miracle,' the people cried (Luke 11: 29), while right in front of them signs and miracles were happening. Of those who demand more and more proof, we need to ask: 'Even if you could be shown absolute proof, would you believe?'

To such people Jesus said: 'Even if someone came back from the dead, you wouldn't believe' (Luke 16: 13 and 31).

If we're honest, the problem of belief is not so much one of ideas and arguments for and against. It's a 'heart' problem — an unwillingness to let go and let God have control.

'What will it cost? People might laugh at me. They'll think I've gone religious on them. It's too late to change now. How do I know Jesus can help me?'

His answer to us is the same as his answer to Jairus, the dead girl's father. 'Don't be afraid. Only believe' (Mark 5: 36).

# STUDY FIVE:
## *Why did Jesus come?*

We have seen that Jesus claimed to be God-become-man. He showed evidence of this when he lived as a man on earth. He had power over death, over the forces of nature, over diseases and suffering. He taught with a knowledge and understanding of the scriptures that the religious leaders themselves didn't have. It was as if he had written the book!

And when his disciples saw him on the mountain, shining with a splendour that belongs only to God, they began to understand that this was the Son of God.

That was a long time ago. Even if God did visit this planet and even if he did do all those wonderful things, what interest is it to me now? If Jesus has anything to say to us, it has to be for today, not two thousand years ago!

The answer to that problem becomes clear when we think about why Jesus came.

 DAY ONE:
## Jesus came to open the way to God
*John 14: 6–7*

*Jesus made claims about himself that really made people sit up and take notice.*

1. Read verse 6 and finish this sentence:
   *Jesus claimed to be:*
   the _____ to God,
   the _____ about God, and
   the _____ in God.

2. Which sentence below is correct?
   ☐ Jesus said he is a way to God.
   ☐ Jesus said he knew the way to God.
   ☐ Jesus said he is the way to God.

3. What are some other ways people try to reach God?

   _____

   _____

   Are there any you have tried personally?

   _____

   _____

4. From verses 6 and 7, finish these sentences:
   If we come to Jesus, we will _____
   the Father.
   If we know Jesus, we will _____
   the Father.
   If we have seen Jesus, we have _____
   the Father.

## ✎ DAY TWO:
## Jesus came to die for our sin
### *John 19: 1–7 and 1 Peter 2: 24*

*Sin is the heart problem of all mankind and none of us has the cure! Sin is our rejection of God's rule in our lives. It separates us from God and condemns us to death. Jesus came to take the death punishment for us, so that we could be given life with God forever.*

*When the time came for Jesus to die, he was arrested by the religious leaders and handed over to the governor for trial.*

5. What did the soldiers seem to think of Jesus
   (verses 2–3)? _____

   _____

   _____

6. What did Governor Pilate think of Jesus (verse 4)?

    _____

    _____

7. What reason did the crowd give for crucifying Jesus (verse 7)? _____

    _____

8. What was the real reason for Jesus' death (1 Peter 2: 24)? _____

    _____

## ✎ DAY THREE:
## Jesus came to bring us to God
*Matthew 27: 45–54*

*Sin separates us from God. This separation is called 'death'. We may be walking around as large as life, but if our sins are not forgiven we are spiritually dead. On the cross, Jesus carried our sin and took the punishment we deserve.*

9. While Jesus was on the cross, two events took place which show the separation from God that sin brings. What were they?
   - ☐ (verse 45) _____
   - ☐ (verse 46) _____

10. After Jesus died, other events happened which show that spiritual death had been beaten. What were they (verses 51–52)? _____

    _____

    _____

11. What was the effect of all this on the soldiers (verse 54)?

    _____

    _____

**DAY FOUR:**
## Jesus came to die according to God's plan
*Isaiah 53: 4–6*

*Jesus' death wasn't a mistake. God planned it. The prophet Isaiah lived about 750 years before Jesus came and he spoke about Jesus' death.*

12. For whom was Jesus to suffer and die (verse 4)?
   _____

13. What was Jesus' death going to gain for us (verse 5)?
   _____

14. What picture does Isaiah use to describe us (verse 6)?
   _____

15. Do you agree with Isaiah or doesn't that picture describe you? _____

 **DAY FIVE:**
## Jesus came to die in my place
*Isaiah 53: 7–10*

*Before Jesus came, lambs were sacrificed to pay for the sin of the people. God accepted these sacrifices as a picture of what Jesus would do for us on the cross. Those sacrifices looked forward to the perfect sacrifice to come.*

16. Did Jesus deserve to die (verse 9)? _____

17. What picture does Isaiah use to describe Jesus (verse 7)?
   _____
   _____

18. The lamb for the sacrifice had to be a perfect one. Why was Jesus able to be our sacrifice (verse 9)?
   _____

19. He has taken the punishment we deserve. In what ways, if any, has this fact changed your life?

_____

_____

## ✎ DAY SIX:
## Jesus came so I could be God's child
### John 1: 10–13

*John calls Jesus 'the Word'.*

20. Verse 10 tells us three things about Jesus ('the Word') and the world. What are they?

_____

_____

_____

21. What must we do in order to be accepted into God's family (verse 12)? _____

_____

22. When we belong to Jesus what can we call God (verse 13)? _____

It was part of the Law God gave to the Jewish nation that every day animals had to be sacrificed for the sin of the people. They knew that sin meant the death penalty and that no-one was good enough or respectable enough to escape.

Jesus came in order to be the once-for-all perfect sacrifice. He came to die according to God's plan. He took the punishment we deserve. He died in our place.

Our self-will cost Jesus his life. To continue in that self-will costs us our eternal life.

We must change *direction* from going against God, rejecting or ignoring him.

We must change *director* — by handing over control of our life to Jesus.

When we put our trust in Jesus, he gives us a new life with God that begins now and goes on with him forever. That's his promise (Romans 6: 23)!

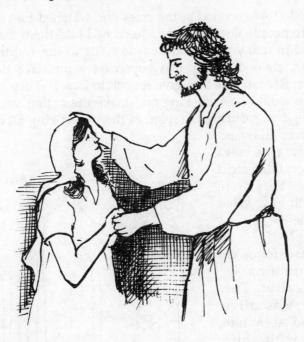

# STUDY SIX:
## *Jesus is alive*

As Jesus' followers stood at the cross and watched him die, they were people without hope. Jesus had told them many times and in many ways that he was going to die, but they hadn't understood. They had hoped he would free their land from Roman rule and give it back to Israel. They had hoped he would be their king and make the nation strong again like it was during the reign of their great king David. Now it was all over.

Only two days later everything had changed. They were filled with joy. What had made the difference?

These followers of Jesus made an incredible claim. They said he was alive. They had seen him, talked with him, touched him (just to make sure he was really real!) and even had meals with him.

Let's look at the event that changed the lives of these ordinary people and which has shaped the course of history ever since: the resurrection of Jesus.

**DAY ONE:**
**The tomb made secure**
Matthew 27: 57–66

*The strange thing was that, even though the disciples hadn't understood Jesus when he said that he would die and come back to life, his enemies heard him loud and clear. They were determined there would be no staging of the big event at their expense.*

1. What did the religious leaders think of Jesus' claim that he would be raised to life (verse 63)? _____

_____

2. What were they expecting to happen (verse 64)?

_____

3. What steps were taken to prevent a break-in (verses 65–66)? _____

_____

The leaders weren't taking any chances. The stone door alone would have been difficult to move. It was huge, dropped down into the doorway of the cave tomb and needing several strong men to shift it. Then there was the guard — anything from ten to thirty soldiers — and the governor's seal — broken on penalty of death.

There was no question in their minds that Jesus was dead. They had done that job brutally and thoroughly. They were just making sure he stayed that way.

 **DAY TWO**
**Seeing is believing**
Luke 24: 1–10

*Jesus had been buried in a hurry because the sabbath holy day was beginning when no-one could work. As soon as the sabbath was ended, some of the women returned to prepare the body properly.*

4.  What three things did the women see when they reached the tomb?
    - ☐ (verse 2) _____
    - ☐ (verse 3) _____
    - ☐ (verse 4) _____

5.  What news did the angels give them (verse 6)?

    _____

6.  What did the women do when they heard this good news (verse 9)? _____

    _____

7.  Wait a minute! What about those super security measures? What happened to the stone?

    _____

    What happened to the governor's seal? _____

    _____

    Where was the guard? (See Matthew 28:2–4 for the full story.)_____

    The leaders had been determined to stop a break-in. They hadn't been counting on a break-*out*!

## ✎ DAY THREE:
## Believing is receiving
*John 20: 24–28*

*After he came back to life, Jesus appeared to many people at different times, in different places — outdoors and indoors. These people weren't imagining things — hallucinations don't happen like that. Here's how Jesus met with Thomas.*

8.  What did Thomas think of the news that Jesus was alive (verse 25)? _____

    _____

9.  How did Jesus deal with Thomas' doubts? _____

    _____

10. What did Jesus tell Thomas to do, when he had proved he was alive (verse 27)? _____

    _____

11. What did Thomas now understand about Jesus (verse 28)? _____

    _____

## ✎ DAY FOUR:
## Receiving is life
*John 20: 29–31*

12. Thomas believed because he saw and touched. What did Jesus say about those like us who don't have that opportunity (verse 29)? _____

    _____

13. Why did John record these things about Jesus (verse 31)? _____

    _____

    _____

Thomas and John were convinced by the evidence
they saw and heard that Jesus is the Son of God.
They were willing to let their lives depend on
that fact.

14. What does the evidence mean to you? _____

_____

## ✎ DAY FIVE:
## Life is belonging
*Romans 5: 6–11*

15. How did God demonstrate his great love for us
    (verse 8)? _____

    _____

16. What has Jesus' death done for those who believe in
    him?
    (verse 9) _____
    (verse 10) _____

17. Read verses 6 to 8. Which sentence is correct?
    ☐ We should try to get our lives in order before we
      ask Jesus' forgiveness.
    ☐ We should come to Jesus for forgiveness and he
      will put our lives in order.

## ✎ DAY SIX:
## Belonging is freedom
*Romans 8: 31–37*

18. The verses below tell us how God cares for those
    who are put right with him through his Son. Note
    the things God does for us:
    (verse 31)  God is _____ us.
    (verse 32)  God will give us _____
    (verse 33)  God will declare us _____

19. What is Jesus doing right now for those who love him (verse 34)? _____

_____

20. What can those who love Jesus be sure of?
(verse 37) _____
(verse 39) _____

The fact that Jesus died is beyond doubt. The fact that he came back to life sends shock waves through history. Look at the facts:

(a) *An empty tomb:* Jesus' body was never produced. To this day that tomb stands empty.

(b) *A dead man seen alive:* There was no doubt that Jesus was dead. The Roman guard said he was (Mark 15: 44–45). Pilate believed he was. The Jewish leaders knew he was (Matthew 27: 62–66), and so did the followers of Jesus.
The medical evidence supports them all. The blood cells and serum had separated (John 19: 34). Yet, from the third day after his death, repeated meetings with Jesus were reported.

(c) *People were changed:* The followers of Jesus, so recently despairing and afraid, now began to proclaim with great courage that Jesus was alive. They had seen him, talked with him, touched him and eaten with him.

At one time he was seen by over 500 people
(1 Corinthians 15: 6). They were prepared to
face persecution, imprisonment, torture and death
to defend what they knew to be true.

Christianity stands or falls on the truth of the resurrection. Faith is not believing the unbelievable, but taking a stand on the facts. Jesus died for our sin, was buried and raised to life again.

As we place our lives in God's hands, accept the forgiveness Jesus gives and receive him as Lord, God gives us a new life that goes on with him forever (John 3: 16).

# STUDY SEVEN: *The Holy Spirit*

Forty days after Jesus came back to life, he returned to heaven (read Acts 1: 3–11). As his disciples watched him ascend into heaven and disappear from view, they may have had mixed feelings. Much had happened during the past month.

Their Lord had been murdered, but was now alive again. The past weeks had been special times of friendship and learning as Jesus explained the scriptures to them and opened their eyes to understand God's plan for his world. Now he was leaving them again.

Yet this time was different from the last. As they stood at the cross watching Jesus die, they were people without hope. As they stood on the hilltop watching Jesus return to his Father, they were people with a promise. Jesus had 'old them: 'I will be with you always, to the end of the age' (Matthew 28: 20).

How was Jesus, who had now left them, going to be with each one — in every cir cumstance, all the time? They were soon to find out. Jesus had promised to send them his Helper, the Holy Spirit who would be in them and give them all they needed to live as God's people in a rebellious world. The promise was fulfilled a short time later on the Day of Pentecost. You can read about it in Acts 2: 1–4.

The promise of the Holy Spirit wasn't just for those disciples of Jesus who lived then. It was a promise for all who commit their lives to Jesus no matter where or when they live. If you have made Jesus Lord of your life, then his Spirit lives in you. Let's think about the Holy Spirit: who he is and what he does.

###  DAY ONE:
### He is a person
*John 16: 7—15*

*The Holy Spirit is not an impersonal force or influence. The Holy Spirit is 'he', not 'it'. He is God the Holy Spirit. In these verses Jesus is teaching his disciples about the Holy Spirit.*

1.  What did Jesus call the Holy Spirit (verse 7)?
    _____

2.  How does this passage show that the Holy Spirit is a person and not just an influence?
    _____
    _____

3.  What does the Holy Spirit do in the world (verse 8)?
    _____
    _____

4.  Jesus couldn't explain everything to the disciples before he died because it was too much for them to understand. What promise did he give them (verse 13)? _____
    _____
    _____

5.   When we accept Jesus as our Lord, we receive the Holy Spirit.  Then, as we read the Bible, he helps us to understand things we couldn't understand before he came to live in us.  In what ways have you found this to be true in your life?

_____

_____

## ✎ DAY TWO:
## He gives life to those who trust Jesus
*Romans 8: 1–8*

*When we read about 'death' in this section, it means separation from God forever, now and after we physically die.  'Life' means being with God forever, beginning from the moment we accept Jesus' forgiveness and make him our Lord.*

6.   What causes 'forever death' (verse 6a)?  _____

_____

7.   What results in 'forever life' (verse 6b)?  _____

_____

8.   Dead people can't bring themselves back to life. Neither can we make ourselves right with God by our own efforts.  How did God make it possible for us to receive the gift of life (verse 3b)?  _____

_____

## ✎ DAY THREE:
## He adopts those who trust in Jesus
*Romans 8: 12—17*

*The Holy Spirit makes us alive in God, which we are unable to do for ourselves.  He brings us into God's family when we accept Jesus as our Saviour.*

9.  What new relationship with God does the Holy
    Spirit give us (verse 14)? _____

    _____

10. What are we then allowed to call God (verse 15)?

    _____

11. What belongs to us because we are God's children
    (verse 17)? _____

    _____

12. Our relationship with God, then, is not a formal,
    uncertain business. It is warm, loving and safe.
    Is this a new truth for you? _____
    How should it affect the way we relate to God?

    _____

    _____

## ✎ DAY FOUR:
## He changes those who trust in Jesus
*Galatians 5: 16–26*

*The Holy Spirit makes us alive in God and he gives us a new
relationship with God as his children. Now that we belong to the
family, he sets about producing in us the family likeness — the
fruit of the Spirit.*

13. Every disease has its symptoms: telltale signs that
    point to its presence. We don't like to think of
    ourselves as sinners, but the symptoms are obvious.
    What are they (verses 19–21)? _____

    _____

14. The fact is we can't have the best of both worlds.
    It's one or the other. We can't be both self-directed
    and Spirit-led. Why (verse 17)? _____

    _____

15. If we belong to Jesus, then others should be able to see evidence — fruit — of that new relationship. We won't stay the same as we always were. What is that evidence or fruit (verses 22–23)? _____

    _____

16. Remember, weeds grow naturally. Fruit is best when cultivated. Which of these fruits need your attention most in your life? _____

    _____

## ✎ DAY FIVE:
## He gives his work to those who trust in Jesus
*1 Corinthians 12: 4–11*

*In the family of God (those who also trust in Jesus), we have many brothers and sisters. Some are easy to love, some aren't. Some agree with us, some don't. Some are young and some are old. Whoever they are, they are family and we are called to serve them. This is a great privilege. The Holy Spirit gives us 'gifts' so that we can do the job.*

17. Is everyone given the same gift of service in our Christian family (verse 5)?

    _____

18. Read verse 7. For what purpose are the gifts given?

    _____

    Is there anyone who does not have a gift of service?

    _____

19. Note the gifts of service named in the verses below:
    (verse 8) _____
    (verse 9) _____
    (verse 10) _____

    _____

There are other gifts not named here but, whatever the gift is that we have, it is given to be *given away* in service to others. Our old life was self-centred. Our new life is Jesus-centred. Have you begun working for Jesus by serving others yet? If so, in what ways? _____

If not, where might you begin? _____

 DAY SIX
## He is God's guarantee to those who trust in Jesus
*2 Corinthians 4: 18 – 5: 5*

20.  What will happen to our earthbound body (verse 1)?

_____

21.  What kind of body will replace it (verse 1)?

_____

22.  What has God given us as a guarantee that this will certainly take place (verse 5)? _____

_____

23.  Read chapter 4, verse 18. What will the wise Christian fix his attention on in this life (verse 18a)?

_____

Why (verse 18b)? _____

_____

When the Holy Spirit came on the Day of Pentecost (Acts 2: 1–4), it was with the sound of a rushing wind and with tongues like flames of fire. It is not like

that for us but, if you have put your trust in Jesus, then you have received the same Holy Spirit they received. Through the Holy Spirit, God has given you everything you need in order to live for him.

Why, then, are we so often weak, lacking in power and direction? It's not because God has let us down, but because we have not been willing to let the Holy Spirit change us. We need to keep coming back to our heavenly Father for forgiveness and help. As long as we keep holding on to ways of living, thinking and speaking which we know to be sinful, the work of the Holy Spirit in our lives is stifled. Is there some area in your life that needs God's forgiveness and help?

The Holy Spirit is God in us. His work is to change us, to make us more like Jesus, to teach and guide us and — at last — to bring us safely home to our heavenly Father. He gives us strength, peace, purpose for living. . . but only as we are prepared to let him have his way day by day, moment by moment.

# STUDY EIGHT:
## *God's word, the Bible*

When we look at our world and beyond it to the universe, we know that there must be a Maker. It simply could not have happened by chance. It has been said: 'To believe that creation just "happened" is as sensible as believing that a dictionary was created through an explosion in a printing shop.'

The universe shouts that God is there — that he is supremely powerful, creative and intelligent. But how can we know anything more about him? Does he want to be known by us? What, if anything, does he expect from us?

We won't find the answers to these kinds of questions by looking at what God has made. We would only be guessing. To know for certain what God is like we would need to be told by God himself. . . and that is what he has done.

God has given us all we need to know about him in a library of books we call the Bible. The Bible contains history, law, poetry, wise sayings, prophecy and letters. It was written over a period of some 1,400 years by more than forty authors.

All these authors gave the same message: God is real, he is perfect (holy), he made us and he wants us to know him personally.

The Bible is not a collection of people's ideas about God. It claims to be God's word about himself, communicated through people to whom he spoke.

## ✎ DAY ONE:
### God's word reveals himself
*Hebrews 1: 1–3*

1.  What does verse 1 tell us about the ways God has communicated in the past? _____

    _____

2.  What is the greatest way God has spoken (verse 2)?

    _____

    _____

3.  What does God show us about himself through Jesus (verse 3a)? _____

    _____

4.  How does verse 3 show us that Jesus' word is very powerful? _____

    _____

## ✎ DAY TWO:
### God's word came in human form
*John 1: 1–5 and 14*

*God has always wanted us to know him. Jesus, God's Son, came to show us what God the Father is like. These verses tell us that all God's communication to us can be summed up in one name: Jesus.*

5.  Verse 14 tells us that God's Word became a person. Who is he? _____

6.  Verses 1–4 tell us a lot about 'the Word'.
    How long has the Word existed (verse 1)?

Who is the Word (verse 1)?

What did God do through the Word (verse 3)?

What do we have because of the Word (verse 4)?
_____and _____

God hasn't left us in the dark. He has allowed us to see what he is like.

7.  The Word became flesh and his name was Jesus. Read verses 1–5 again. Is there anything new that you have realised about Jesus from this? _____

✎ DAY THREE:
## God's word is true
*Luke 1: 1–4*

*Since Jesus is the focus of all God's communication to us, it was important that what Jesus said and did should be written down accurately. Those, like us, who live many years later need to be sure that these things are not legends or made-up stories, but the truth. Luke was a Christian doctor who reported the life of Jesus.*

8.  Where did Luke get the information for his report (verse 2)? _____

9.  How did Luke go about recording this information (verse 3)? _____

10. Why did he record it (verse 4)?

## ✎ DAY FOUR:
## God's word changes lives
### 2 Timothy 3: 14—17

*The Bible does not contain the word of God. Rather, all of it is the word of God — it is inspired. The Greek word translated 'inspired' (verse 16) means 'God-breathed'. The Bible comes from the mind of God, so it deserves our serious attention.*

11.  How were the scriptures (the books of the Bible) written (verse 16)? _____
     _____

12.  What must we be sure to do (verse 14)? _____
     _____

13.  What can the scriptures do for us if we live by them (verse 17)? _____
     _____

14.  In what ways have you found this to be true? _____
     _____

## ✎ DAY FIVE:
## God's word lasts forever
### 1 Peter 1: 23–25

*It is 1900 years since the last book of the Bible was written. Times change. Ideas and fashions change. Does this mean that God's word is out-of-date for our modern world?*

15.  How long will God's word remain true (verse 25)? _

     Will it therefore ever be out-of-date? _____
     Can it therefore be true for some people, but not for others? _____
     _____

16. Why is it foolish to follow man-made ideas and values (verse 24)? _____

_____

17. In what areas of life has the word of God begun to change your ideas and values? _____

_____

## ✎ DAY SIX:
## God's word sets us free
### James 1: 22–25

*We must never allow our Bible-reading to become only an exercise of the mind. Knowing about God is not the same thing as knowing God. That involves a day-by-day relationship.*

18. What warning are we given in verse 22?

_____

_____

19. In what way does a person who only listens to God's word deceive himself (verses 22–24)?

_____

_____

20. Verse 25 gives us three actions to take in order to benefit from God's word. What are they?
    (a) _____
    (b) _____
    (c) _____

21. What are the results of obeying God's word (verse 25)?

_____

_____

The Bible is God's message to us. He tells us what he is like, what he has done for us and what he expects of us.

The verse 2 Timothy 3: 16 tells us that all scripture is 'breathed by God'. That's why we can call the Bible 'God's word'. Through the Holy Spirit, God put into people's minds what he wanted them to say and they in turn wrote down God's message — not just for their generation, though it was for them, but for all people for all time.

God's greatest and most obvious communication with us was in Jesus: he who was God-become-man. God's word, the Bible, *tells* us about God's love and truth and holiness. Jesus, the Word of God, *demonstrated* God's love and truth and holiness.

The purpose of the Bible is not only to show us what God is like, but to show us ourselves as he sees us. It points us to Jesus, who has made it possible for us to be forgiven and to begin a new life with God as our Father. In order to live for God, we have to let the Holy Spirit change us. He changes us as we read the word of God and take action on it.

We need to read God's word regularly, every day, just as we eat regular meals every day. These studies are to help you form the habit of daily Bible-reading. There are a number of Bible-reading helps as well as useful introductory books to the Bible available from Christian bookshops.

God's word never changes because God never changes. It is true for everyone, everywhere, at all times, yet it is as up-to-date as tomorrow's newspaper. God's word is alive and active. Are you letting it change you?

# STUDY NINE:
## *Prayer — talking with God*

Prayer is probably the most misunderstood and neglected part of our lives as God's people. 'How do I pray? I don't know what to say.' 'Why pray when God already knows what I need?'

Sometimes we think of prayer as a *begging* letter to God, or like giving him our shopping list of what we want him to do for us.

Sometimes we feel we can't come to him because we think we're too *bad* and he won't listen to us.

Sometimes we're just too lazy or too busy to pray. We let other things clutter our time, so that prayer gets pushed out. The urgent takes the place of the important, crowding in on us, convincing us that we don't have time to pray.

How different our lives could be if only we put first things first. As we pray, we have the opportunity to talk with God the mighty Creator who is our heavenly Father.

Prayer is a great privilege because the Father promises to hear and answer every prayer his children pray (1 John 5: 13–15). That is not so for everyone. While most people pray at some time in their lives, the only prayer of the non-Christian God promises to hear is the prayer asking for forgiveness, turning his life over to Jesus (Romans 10: 13).

Since we have such a great privilege, how then should we pray?

##  DAY ONE:
## Pray with confidence
### Hebrews 4: 14–16 and 7: 27

*In the Jewish Temple worship, the high priest was the one who offered sacrifices for the people. He was the 'go-between' with God the Father on their behalf.*

1.  Who is our high priest (verse 14)?

    _____

    What was the sacrifice he made for us (chapter 7, verse 27)? _____

    _____

    _____

2.  How can we be sure that Jesus understands how we feel, the pressures we are under, our joys and disappointments (verse 15)?

    _____

    _____

    _____

    _____

3.  How can we know he is strong enough to help us (verse 15)?

    _____

    _____

    _____

4.  What two things do we receive when we come to
    God in prayer (verse 16b)?
    (a) _____

    _____
    (b) _____

    _____
    (*Grace* means 'God's love freely given to us'.)

✎ **Day Two:**
**Pray about everything**
*Philippians 4: 6–7*

5.  What is the opposite of prayer (verse 6a)?

    _____

    _____

6.  From verse 6, what are we to worry about?

    _____

    And what are we to pray about?

    _____

    _____

7.  What do you think it means to pray with a thankful
    heart? _____

    _____

8.  If we make prayer an important part of our life,
    what does God give us (verse 7)?

    _____

    _____

✎ **Day Three:**
**Pray like Jesus**
*Matthew 6: 7–14*

9.   Is God impressed by the words we use or how we
     plan our sentences when we pray (verse 7)? _____
     Why? _____
     Jesus gave his friends a pattern for praying when he
     gave them the Lord's Prayer.

10.  What three things should we want for God
     (verses 9–10]?
     (a) _____
     (b) _____
     (c) _____

11.  What three things should we ask for ourselves?
     (verse 11) _____
     (verse 12) _____
     (verse 13) _____

12.  What is the condition here for our being forgiven by
     God (verse 12)? _____
     _____
     _____
     Do you think that's fair? _____
     Why?/Why not? _____
     _____

## ✎ DAY FOUR:
### Pray expecting answers
*1 John 5: 14–15*

13.  What can God's people be sure of when they pray
     (verse 15)? _____
     _____

14.  Does that mean God will give us whatever we want?
     Why?/Why not (verse 14)? _____
     _____

15. Which sentence is correct:
    ❐ God will give us whatever we ask for as long as
    we believe hard enough.
    ❐ God will give us whatever we ask because he
    wants us to be happy.
    ❐ God will give us whatever we ask if it is
    according to his will.

*God loves us too much to give us everything we ask for. When*
*we bring all our concerns to God, and pray according to his will,*
*we are really saying that God knows best and we trust him to do*
*the wisest thing. God sees the 'big picture'. His answer is*
*always far better than our small requests. We trust him to say*
*'no', 'wait' or 'yes' according to what he knows is best.*

## ✏ DAY FIVE:
## Pray honestly
*Psalm 66: 16–20*

16. Who are those who can expect help from God
    (verse 16)? _____
    _____

17. There is one condition on which God will not listen
    to our prayer. What is that (verse 18)?
    _____
    _____

18. If we are honest with God, what can we expect
    from him (verse 20)? _____
    _____

*There's no use coming to God and putting on an act, pretending*
*to be something we aren't. He sees straight through us, so we*
*had better drop the 'religious bit' and come clean. With God,*
*honesty is the best policy!*

## ✎ DAY SIX:
## Pray for others
*Ephesians 3: 14–19*

*In this beautiful prayer, the church planter — Paul — is praying for Christians in the church in Ephesus.*

19. What special things was Paul asking from God for the Christians at Ephesus?
    (verse 16) _____
    (verse 17) _____
    _____
    (verse 18) _____
    (verse 19) _____

20. Which of those requests would you most like someone to pray for you? _____
    _____

*It's easy to be lazy when we pray for others. 'God bless' everyone doesn't mean much to us, so how can it achieve much for them? In prayer, we have the opportunity to have a special input for good into the lives of others, an input that will have value for eternity.*

21. What steps can you take to make sure that you pray meaningfully for others?
    _____
    _____

Prayer is our person-to-Person, direct line to God our Father. We can call any time. He is never 'out to lunch' or too busy to listen. He answers personally and we never have to worry that our concerns are unimportant to him. We are the King's children and that makes us special to him.

Why pray at all? First, because God has told us to pray, and that should be reason enough. But there is more to it than that. If we are serious about wanting to know God, then we will spend time with him, letting him speak to us through his word and sharing our lives with him through prayer. We can't claim to know someone we never talk to! The way any friendship deepens is by friends spending time together, getting to know each other in all situations.

What do we pray about? Absolutely everything! We can plan our prayer time by remembering to say:

☐ **Thank you.** Begin positively. Remember what God has done for you. It will encourage you to keep praying and build up your faith. We are easily discouraged, so take note of answered prayer — perhaps even keep a note book.

☐ **Sorry.** We need to keep short accounts with God. Sin admitted is sin forgiven.

☐ **Please.** We need to pray for ourselves, for everything that concerns us — family relationships, work, personal decisions. Nothing is too small for God to deal with and nothing is too big for him to manage.
And we have a responsibility to pray for others, especially our family and those we know well. Keep a diary. You may not pray for everyone every day, but try to do so regularly.

Jesus' prayer is the perfect model for our prayer times and Paul's prayer for the Ephesians is a great one to use for Christian friends. So. . . find a quiet place where you can have some time to yourself (not always easy!) and make a start.

# STUDY TEN:
## *God's people — the church*

Today in the Western world, less people than ever before attend church. While most believe there is a God, they don't see the church as having a place in their lives. They see it as unimportant, unnecessary and out of touch. You often hear it said:

'After all, you don't have to go to church to be a Christian.'

'The church is full of hypocrites.'

'I'd feel awkward going to church. I'm not good enough.'

'Hey, the day I go to church the roof will fall in!'

What is the church? Is it a building? An organisation? A club? Is it out-of-date in the twentieth century?

The Bible tells us that, when we belong to Jesus, we become one of God's people, the family of God (John 1: 12–13). The church is not somewhere we go, but who we are all together. Wherever the people of God are, there is the church. The Bible gives us some great pictures to help us understand what this means.

## ✎ DAY ONE:
## The church — a separated people
### 1 Peter 2: 9–12

1. What four names are given to God's people in verse 9?
   (a) _____
   (b) _____
   (c) _____
   (d) _____

2. What has God done to make us his people?
   (verse 9b) _____
   (verse 10b) _____

3. How are we to see ourselves in this world
   (verse 11a)?

   _____

4. How, then, should we live in the world if this is
   what we are (verses 11b and12)? _____

   _____

## ✎ DAY TWO:
## The church — a united people
### Acts 2: 44–47

5. What impresses you most about the church in this
   passage?

   _____

   _____

6. What things did the church do together?
   (verse 44a) _____
   (verse 44b–45) _____
   (verses 46a) _____
   (verse 46b) _____

7.   What was the result of this way of life (verse 47b)?

      _____

      _____

8.   Why do you think other people were attracted to them and became Christians? _____

      _____

## ✎ DAY THREE:
## The church — a built up people
### Ephesians 2: 19–22

*'Gentiles' means anyone who isn't a Jew (verse 19).*

9.   Verse 21 describes God's people as a building. What kind of building do they form? _____

      _____

*The cornerstone was either a very large stone put in place first, in a corner position, so that the rest of the building could be measured from it, or it was the top and centre stone in an archway, which balanced and held in place the other stones.*

10.  Who is the church's corner-stone (verse 20)?

      _____

      _____

11.  What does the picture of a corner-stone say to you about him?

      _____

      _____

Just as one brick standing alone doesn't make a building, so God's people are not to stand alone.

12. Who do we stand with in order to be God's building (verse 22)? _____

## ✎ DAY FOUR:
### The church — a whole people
*1 Corinthians 12: 12–20*

13. What is the picture used here to describe God's people (verse 12)? _____

_____

14. Who made us all different from each other (verse 18)?

_____

15. In God's church is anyone:
   ☐ unnecessary?

   ☐ unimportant?

   _____

   ☐ more important than others?

   _____

16. What do you think happens to 'Christ's body' when one person acts as if. . .
   ☐ he/she isn't important?

   _____

   _____

   ☐ he/she is more important than others?

   _____

   _____

## ✎ DAY FIVE:
## The church — a loving people
1 Corinthians 13: 1–7

17. What is the first responsibility of all Christians to each other (verses 1–3)? _____

_____

18. The Bible tells us 'God is love' (1 John 4: 8). Read verses 4 to 7 saying 'God is. . .' instead of 'Love is. . .' What does this say to you about your heavenly Father? _____

_____

Love is the way we treat other people rather than the feelings we have about them. We are to *show* God's love to his hurting world.

19. Now read verses 4–7 with 'I am. . .' instead of 'Love is. . .' (Remember, this means *always* — not just when we're in a good mood!)
Did you choke? We all fail miserably, don't we? Which areas do you need to work on?

_____

_____

## ✎ DAY SIX:
## The church — a responsible people
Hebrews 10: 23—25

20. What responsibilities do we have to each other?
(verse 24) *Let us* _____
(verse 25) *Let us not* _____
          *Let us* _____

22. Can a Christian fulfil his responsibility to God and his people if he fails to meet with them regularly?

Why/Why not? _____

_____

23.  What fact should encourage us to act responsibly as
     God's people (verse 25b)? _____

     _____

We usually think of the church as that building down the
street. That's not God's church. God's church is people —
those who love Jesus and who want to live for him. If that
is true of you, then you are a member of God's family, the
church. Just think how many brothers and sisters you have
all over the world!

   Let's think about the pictures God gives us of his
church. We are:

☐ **A separated people.** We are God's nation. He is
   our king. A nation has its own laws and
   standards by which it operates. Ours is the
   Bible, the word of God. A nation is supposed to
   work together for the good of the whole. God's
   people are to commit themselves to one another.

☐ **A building.** It's a
   special building, a
   temple, and we are
   the bricks. The
   Temple was the
   place where God
   was said to live
   among his people.
   We are set apart,
   together with each
   other, as God's
   special place to live.
   We are to bring
   honour to him.

❑ **The body.** This tells us that we are each important and we each have a job to do for God.
No-one is left out.
Have you noticed how much you become aware
of your little toe when it hurts? That's how your
local church fellowship is when you don't
belong. We make the *whole* body hurt.

The church, God's people, has the responsibility of
showing the family likeness to the world. We are to grow
more like our Father every day. When others want to see
what God is like, they should be able to look at his people
and say: 'There he is! That is what God is like!'

We don't *go* to church. We *are* the church. We go to
meet with the church. We need to ask ourselves: am I
being a responsible member of God's family, or am I still
only wrapped up in my own interests?

For God's people, 'church' is not an optional extra.
It's part of the deal, the whole package.

# STUDY ELEVEN: *Growing a happy family*

Perhaps the hardest place to live out our faith in Jesus and our love for him is in our family, among the ones who know us best. They see us in our unguarded moments. They know the best and the worst of us. We may be able to present a good image to the world, but what if it falls to pieces as soon as we step in our own front door?

When we accept Jesus' rule in our lives the first ones who should benefit from the change are our own families. How aweful it is if we prove to be a saint in the world and a monster at home. Jesus is not at all impressed by Christians with split personalities. He looks at the attitudes of our hearts at all times.

Perhaps there are relationships that need to be mended: wives who need love, husbands who need respect, children who need to be accepted for who they are. Where those problems are deep and long-standing Christian counselling should be looked for. To begin, there are two important rules for shaping a happy home:

1. I must take responsibility for changing my attitudes. I must be willing to change first, not wait for others to change before I do.

2. I need to know what God says about families. Then I know where to start.

Are we ready, then, to take a close look at ourselves within our families? Are we committed to making changes in this area, even if those changes are painful? We are not to read God's word to find out all the things our husband or wife needs to know, but to allow God to begin his work in us.

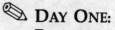

### DAY ONE:
**Parents**
*Matthew 15: 3–6 and 10: 37*

*In Matthew 15: 3–6, Jesus is talking to adults who are trying to sidestep their responsibility to their ageing parents.*

1. How are we to treat our parents (verse 4)?_____
   _____

2. How do we know that God takes this very seriously (verse 4)? _____
   _____

3. Does this rule apply only to 'good' parents?
   _____

4. From what this passage tells us, how should we care for our parents when they are in need?
   _____
   _____

   As adults we show respect for parents by caring for them and watching out for their well-being. As children we show respect by obeying our parents. Read Matthew 10: 37.

5. Children are to love and respect their parents, but, to whom must we give our first loyalty?_____
   _____

6. When is it right for children to disobey parents?
   _____

### DAY TWO:
**Marriage**
*Matthew 19: 3–6*

*When adult children marry and leave home, the relationship with their parents changes. Their loyalty is now to their partner first, not their parents.*

7.  Whose plan was marriage (verse 4)?_____

    _____

8.  When was marriage introduced (verse 4)?_____

    _____

9.  When a couple marries, what two things must they do (verse 5)?
    (a)  _____
    (b)  _____

10. What happens if they are careful to do both these things (verses 5–6)?  _____

    _____

11. What do you think it means to 'become one'?

    _____

    _____

    The unwillingness of a marriage partner to 'leave Mum and Dad' in terms of loyalty can cause big problems. The unwillingness of a parent to 'let go' can also cause trouble.

12. How can a couple deal with a situation where a parent tries to interfere in a marriage?  (Remember, we are to respect our parents.) _____

    _____

    _____

 **Day Three**
**Wives**
*Ephesians 5: 21–30 and Matthew 20: 26*

13. What do you think it means to 'submit' (Matthew 20: 26)? _____

    _____

14. Who is to submit to whom (verse 21)?_____

    _____

15. How does a husband submit to his wife (verse 28)?

    _____

    _____

16. How does a wife submit to her husband (verse 24)?

    _____

    _____

17. What are some things a wife can wrongly allow to come between her and her husband?

    _____

    _____

## ✎ DAY FOUR:
## Husbands
*Ephesians 5: 21–30*

18. How much is a husband to love his wife?
    (verse 25) _____
    (verse 28) _____

19. Who has the final authority in the partnership (verse 23)? _____

20. What kind of authority is it (verses 28–29)?

    _____

21. What are some of the things a husband can wrongly allow to come between him and his wife?

    _____

    _____

# ✎ DAY FIVE:
## Parenting
*Ephesians 6: 4*

22. What are the two things Christians must have as the foundation of their parenting? _____

   _____

   Christian discipline should be fair, firm and carried out in love. Punishment is only a part of discipline. To discipline a child is to set the limits within which the child is free to move. It involves praise, affection, encouragement and firmness.

23. What are parents to avoid? _____

   _____

   Christian discipline tells a child *what* the limits are. Christian instruction tells the child *why* the limits are. More than anything else, Christian parents will want their children to know Jesus as their Friend.

24. How are you instructing your children about Jesus?

   _____

   _____

25. How does your church support you in the instruction of your children? _____

   _____

   One of the first jobs we have to do after we accept Jesus' rule in our lives is to sort out our relationships. In this age of instant everything there are no instant family-fixers, but there are guidelines. If we invite Jesus to take charge, and do our part by following the guidelines God has given us, we will begin to see results.

*Parents* are to take their job seriously, on behalf of Jesus, and to do so for the child's benefit, not their own convenience or ambitions.

*Children* are to respect their parents and obey them.

*Husbands* are to exercise leadership in the home. They are to give of themselves, rather than just provide 'things', just as Jesus gives himself to us.

*Wives* are to recognise the task God has given to their husbands and with gentleness, respect and love be an encouragement to them.

The family is a team where each member has a part to play. No one is more or less important than another. Problems arise when one member plays his own game regardless of the others, or breaks the rules, or tries to boss everyone around, or won't pull his weight on the team.

Those who are single parents know how hard it is to manage when the team is short of a key player. You will find real support if you depend on Jesus to get you through and find a church fellowship where you will be helped and encouraged.

When we allow Jesus to teach us and change us within our family, renewing relationships, putting wrong right, then we will find we are far better able to serve him in the world. How does the building up begin? With the first step you take!

# STUDY TWELVE: *A right mind*

The hardest place to live out our commitment to Jesus may often be in our home, but probably the most confusing place is in society. We no longer live in a society with a firm moral foundation. What is believed to be moral depends on what the majority accepts. This is called 'consensus morality' and is often judged by which group makes the loudest noise about it.

Truth has become a word without meaning. We are told that one thing can be true for you, while the opposite is true for me — and we must both be allowed to be correct. In our society, to have a definite point of view is 'narrow-minded'. To consider certain forms of behaviour as 'wrong' is said to be judgmental and unloving.

That kind of thinking leaves Christians in a poor light. They must be by society's definition 'narrow-minded', 'judgmental' and 'unloving'.

It is no wonder, then, that Christians often find it easier to just back off and keep quiet. It is far more comfortable to go along with the crowd. No-one likes to be seen as the bad guy.

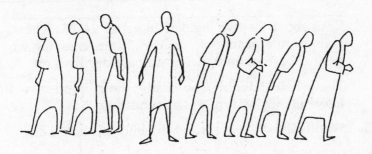

Our society has lost its way. We no longer have a firm foundation on which to build. We make it up as we go along. It has been said: 'Our grandparents told us, "Love God and do good." Our parents told us, "Do good" and our generation asks, "Why?"' Once people lose sight of God, there is no standard by which truth can be accurately measured. Your guess is as good as mine.

Because they are God's people, Christians must know what God has said. These are his rules, not ours. Jesus said, 'If you love me, you will obey my commandments' (John 14: 15). That means, if our relationship with Jesus doesn't direct our lives, then it is not a relationship at all. Let's look at some of the burning issues in our society and see what God says about them and why.

 **DAY ONE:**
## God demands obedience
*Matthew 7: 21–27*

1. Talk means very little. What does Jesus look for in those who claim to believe in him (verse 21)?

   _____

2. On judgment day, what will Jesus say to those who have talked the God-talk, put on a great act, but have not been careful to obey God (verse 23)?

   _____

Read about the two builders in verses 24–27. The houses are a picture of our lives. Jesus is saying we must choose carefully what we base our lives on.

The whole building, no matter how impressive it looks, is only as firm as its foundation.

3. Who is like the wise man who built his house on

rock (verse 24)?

_____

4.  Who is like the foolish man who built his house on
    sand (verse 26)?

    _____

    It is better to live in a cottage built on rock, than a
    mansion built on shifting ground.

 ## DAY TWO:
## Drug abuse
*Proverbs 23: 21, 29–30 and 1 Corinthians 6:19–20*

*When we think of drug abuse, the drugs which probably come
to mind are those which are illegal, such as heroin, cocaine,
crack or marihuana. The results of these are tragic, but the
drugs which are most commonly used — and which cause the
most widespread damage in society — are the legal ones:
tobacco and alcohol.*

5.  What bad effects of alcohol abuse are mentioned in
    these verses from Proverbs chapter 23?
    (a)  verse 21 _____

    _____

    (b)  verses 29–30 _____

    _____

    Read 1 Corinthians 6: 19–20.

6.  When we accept Jesus as Lord, we can no longer
    say, 'I can do what I like with my own body.'
    (a)  Who now lives in our bodies?

    _____

    (b)  Who now owns our bodies?

    _____

    (c)  For what purpose are we now to use our

bodies?

_____

_____

 **DAY THREE:**
**Divorce**
*Matthew 19: 3–9*

Divorce in Jesus' day was as easy as it is now. That wasn't God's original plan.

7.   In your own words, what was Jesus' answer to the Pharisees' first question (verses 4–6)?

_____

_____

8.   Why did God allow divorce (verse 8)?

_____

_____

9.   What answer did Jesus give to those who take divorce lightly (verse 9)?

_____

_____

10.  Is unhappiness or boredom in marriage a good enough reason to divorce? _____
How might these problems be dealt with?

_____

_____

 **DAY FOUR:**
**Sexuality abuse**

*We have read in the last section that God made us sexual beings and that he intended us to enjoy that expression within the security of a lifelong commitment between a man and a woman.*

**Sexual immorality**
Read the verses below from 1 Corinthians chapter 6.

11. Read verses 12–14. For what purpose is the body *not* to be used (verse 13)?

_____

For what purpose *is* the body to be used?

_____

12. Read verses 9–10. Is it acceptable to God for a person who has committed his/her life to Jesus to live in an immoral relationship _____ Why/Why not? _____

_____

Read Romans 1: 18–32.

13. How can people know the truth about God (verse 20)? _____

_____

14. What prevents the truth being known (verses 18, 21 and 23)? _____

_____

15. What sins follow from refusing the truth about God (verses 24–31)? _____

_____

## ✎ DAY FIVE:
## Abortion
*Psalm 139: 13–16*

15. What does this passage tell us about the unborn child (verses 13 and 15)?

_____

_____

16. How does this passage show us that no person is 'unwanted' or an 'accident' — and that means *you* (verses 15—16)? _____

_____

17. How would you answer these statements which are often used to justify abortion?
    (a) 'A woman has the right to decide what happens to her own body.'
       *Note:* Is the baby a part of her body — like her arm or liver? See verse 13.

       _____

       _____

       _____

    (b) 'Before a certain number of weeks, the foetus cannot be considered as being human. It is a piece of tissue.' Compare verse 15.

       _____

       _____

## ✎ DAY SIX:
## Watching what we watch
### Matthew 6: 22–23

*The impact of television on our home life has been enormous. The number of video outlets is growing rapidly. 'Soft porn' magazines line newsagent shelves. Does it matter what we watch?*

18. What does Jesus say about our eyes (verse 22a)?

_____

19. How does this passage answer those who claim that what one watches has no effect on how one thinks or acts? _____

_____

20. Are you exercising wisdom over the TV program-
    mes, videos and movies you and your children
    watch? What steps do you take to do so? _____

_____

*The problem* is that we live in a society that has no
measuring line, no firm foundation for making moral
decisions.

*The result* is a lot of confused people with too many
minds to decide anything and no sense of direction.

*The answer* is the same as it has always been:

(a) God has made us and has given us groundrules
    for successful living.

(b) God has given us these groundrules for our
    benefit so that we will know what he is like

and how he expects us to live. They are not
optional extras like the trim on a car door.
They are the only way to live.

(c)  God is love.  God is holy.  We cannot choose to
have God's love, but ignore his holiness.  We
are loved by the holy God who has every right
to demand our obedience.  Jesus said, 'If you
love me, you will keep my commandments'
(John 14: 15).

It's not easy to make
changes and break old
habits.  But as we get to
know God's word better, we
must change our minds to fit
in with God's way of think
ing — and that will change
our attitudes and behaviour.

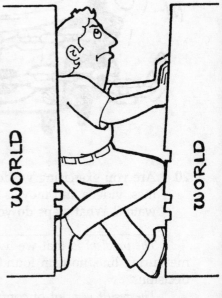

It's not easy because it
takes time to learn — and a
willingness to grow and
change.  We will be learning
and growing for the rest of
our lives.

It's not easy because
obedience means standing
up for what we know to be
true even when it is un-
popular or makes us look
foolish.

It's not easy because there are times when we would
much rather have a God that makes us feel comfortable,
rather than belong to One who keeps challenging us to
conform to him (Romans 12: 21).

We will let him down.  We will fail. . . but, because

Jesus has bought us for himself, we don't stop belonging to him. We are members of God's forever family. Failure is never final as long as there is the willingness to admit failure (something some of us find very hard to do), ask forgiveness and keep going.

If we are willing to do that, then we can be sure that 'God, who began this good work in you, will carry it on until it is finished on the day of Christ Jesus' (Philippians 1: 6).

# NOTES

# NOTES

# NOTES

# NOTES

# NOTES

# NOTES

# NOTES

# NOTES

# NOTES